Editor: Heather Dickson

Authors: Nick Daws (Mystery in Nepal, Shipwrecked, Death on Kilimanjaro, Around the World in Seven Lies and The Lost Idol), Christine Pountney (Going for Gold, Bridging the Gap, The Gold Pendant, Greta and the Gunslinger, Highly Strung and Extreme Measures) and Richard Skinner (A Run-in with Death)

Additional contributors: Lorna O'Connell, Russell Walton, Peter Kirkham, Rosie Atkins

Illustrator: Anni Jenkins

Page layout: Linley Clode

Cover design: Gary Inwood Studios

Published by: LAGOON BOOKS
PO BOX 311, KT2 5QW, UK

ISBN : 1899712348

Printed in France.

FIVE-MINUTE
ADVENTURE
LATERAL THINKING
PUZZLES

OTHER TITLES

Five-Minute Lateral Thinking Puzzle Books

Five-Minute Murder Lateral Thinking Puzzles ISBN 189971233X
Five-Minute Classic Lateral Thinking Puzzles ISBN 1899712291
Five-Minute Crime Lateral Thinking Puzzles ISBN 1899712283

Mind-Bending Puzzle Books

Mind-Bending Lateral Thinking Puzzles ISBN 1899712062
More Mind-Bending Lateral Thinking Puzzles - Volume II
ISBN 1899712194
Mind-Bending Lateral Thinking Puzzles by Des MacHale
ISBN 1899712232
Mind-Bending Conundrums and Puzzles ISBN 1899712038
Mind-Bending Classic Logic Puzzles ISBN 1899712186
Mind-Bending Challenging Logic Puzzles ISBN 1899712240
Mind-Bending Classic Word Puzzles ISBN 1899712054
Mind-Bending Crossword Puzzles ISBN 1899712399

All books can be ordered from bookshops by
quoting the above ISBN numbers.
Some titles may not be available in all countries.
All titles are available in the UK.

INTRODUCTION

This book contains a pocketful of some of the greatest lateral thinking puzzles, ingeniously disguised in a collection of action-packed and peril-filled adventure stories.

Each of the highly amusing stories is set in a different corner of the globe and tells of the chance encounters and hazardous tales of 12 different adventurers.

They take only five minutes to read - how long it will take to answer the question posed at the end of each story, depends on whether you work it out for yourself, or resort to deciphering the mirror writing solution provided after each story.

(The answer to each puzzle is in mirror writing - this will stop an accidental glance spoiling the fun. Just hold the page up to a mirror for the answer to be revealed.)

INDEX

MYSTERY IN NEPAL

MYSTERY IN NEPAL

As soon as Phil Benton got home he poured himself a large Jack Daniel's. He needed it after the day at the office he'd just had. So he was not best pleased when, just as he had collapsed in his favourite armchair, the phone rang.

"Phil! Hiya, buddy, how're you doing?"

Despite himself, Phil smiled. "Hi, Billy," he said. "I've had better days. How about you?"

"I'm great, man. I just got back from my vacation in Nepal."

"Oh yeah, I remember." Phil took a sip of the whiskey. As the warming nectar slipped down his throat, he felt himself starting to unwind. "The great adventure. Well, how did it go?"

"It was amazing, man, amazing. The country, the people, the places. And I've got the most incredible story to tell you."

"Why, what happened?" Phil realised that Billy sounded excited, even for Billy. "Don't tell me - you found the Abominable Snowman?"

"No, no - better than that."

Phil waited, but Billy said no more. "Well, what then?"

"I'll bet you anything you'll never guess. Can you get down to Deano's Bar at seven tonight? The rest of the gang will be there."

Phil eyed the whiskey bottle regretfully. He had been looking forward to a quiet night in with the Jack Daniel's and David

Letterman. On the other hand, if the big build-up was anything like justified, this should be a story well worth hearing.

"OK," he said. "Seven o'clock it is."

As he made his way across town to Deano's, Phil found himself wondering what kind of tale Billy would spin tonight. Knowing his friend, betting would figure somewhere in it. Billy loved to bet, though his wagers were always small: often just a bottle of Bud or one of Deano's 'Dino' Burgers. The most Phil had ever seen Billy bet was fifty bucks, and that was when he must have known he was onto a winner.

Yet hadn't he said, "I'll bet you anything you won't guess", on the phone? By Billy's standards, that was reckless to the point of insanity. Phil quickened his pace. This could be interesting, he thought. He turned left, and was greeted by the familiar red neon sign marking the entrance to Deano's Bar. He skipped down the steps two at a time.

At this early hour the bar was quiet. Deano himself was behind the counter, polishing glasses. He grinned when he saw Phil, and nodded towards their usual table, under the 'Beer on Tap' sign, where Billy was already holding court. Gathered around him, Phil recognised Jeff, Lisa, Randy, Paula, Cindy and Mal. Billy stopped as he saw Phil approach.

"Phil. Pull up a stool. I was just telling the guys about Nepal, but I'll start again now you're here."

Phil grinned. "OK. Let me just get a drink."

"Hey, this one's on me." Billy raised his voice. "Deano! A bottle of your finest beer for my good friend Phil!"

Phil took a stool next to Lisa, who was looking drop-dead gorgeous in a pair of faded jeans and a cropped T-shirt. She gave him a smile, and Phil felt his mood lighten still further. Deano handed over his drink, and he took a large gulp before setting it down on the table.

Billy beamed round his circle of friends. "Well, now I can tell you the whole story. Like I said, I wanted to do something really different on my vacation this year, so I hit on the idea of Nepal. In case you don't know, it's in the southern Himalayas, wedged between China to the north and India to the south."

"I know," Mal said. "Mount Everest's there, right?"

"Is that the big story?" Cindy asked, grinning. "While you were there, you climbed it?"

"Very funny," Billy said. "I'll tell you everything, if you'll just give me a chance. I flew into the capital, Kathmandu.
I stayed at a hotel in the city for a few days, just to acclimatise and see a few of the sites."

"What was it like?" Randy asked.

"Pretty amazing, if you want the truth. The streets are lined by pagodas, stupas and stone sculptures..."

"What's a stupa?" Lisa wanted to know.

"A domed building containing religious relics," Phil told her. Lisa looked suitably impressed.

"Yeah," Billy said. "Like you say. And, inside, the rooms are crammed with horror masks, spinning prayer wheels, thangka scrolls and Tibetan carpets. And everywhere you go in Nepal you hear music: from hymns and chants, to flutes and four-stringed saringhi."

"It sounds exotic, all right," Paula said. "Did you go into the mountains?"

"I was coming to that," Billy said. He took another gulp. "After a few days I felt reasonably acclimatised, so I decided to hit the trail. I headed for Pokhara, a beautiful place with a lake on one side and the mountains on the other. From Pokhara you can see Annapurna, the first eight-thousand-metre peak ever climbed, Mount Dhaulagiri and Mount Kanchenjunga - with its five peaks which dominate the skyline.

"Anyway, I took a room in a guesthouse in Pokhara, and the next morning loaded up my backpack and headed into the mountains. And it was there, in the foothills of the Himalayas, that I met Rami." He paused for a moment. "Uh, my glass seems to be empty."

Everyone looked up, but Phil was first to catch the barman's eye. "Another Molson, please, Deano."

"Sure thing, Phil." Deano opened another bottle and brought it over. "Another beer for the great adventurer."

"Thanks, buddy." Billy drank deeply, and wiped his mouth with his sleeve. "Man, all this talking sure gives you a thirst!" He looked round to ensure he still had everyone's undivided attention.

"Well, like I said, I met Rami. I was walking up this mountain track, and he was simply standing there, staring out across the lake and the mountains. Do you know what first struck me about him?" No one offered any suggestions, so he continued: "It was his air of perfect happiness. He looked like a man who had won the state lottery, married Miss America and been awarded the Pulitzer Prize, all on the same day."

Everyone laughed, and Cindy said, "Whatever he was on, I hope you brought some back for the rest of us!"

Billy smiled. "OK, I might have had the same thought, but I soon discovered it was nothing as simple as that. For one thing, he had this almost child-like innocence about him. Yet he sure wasn't immature or simple-minded. He spoke at least five different languages. And, as I soon discovered, that was by no means the full extent of his special talents."

Again Billy paused to drink. "I hadn't been feeling too good that day. I'd woken up with a bad headache, perhaps a migraine, and as the day went on it got worse. As I walked up that mountain track towards him, do you know what I heard him say? 'Brother, let me heal your pain.'

"He said it so softly, I wondered at first whether he was talking to me at all. Yet I heard the words quite clearly. Then he turned towards me, and his face lit up with the most radiant smile I've ever seen - like the sun coming out from behind dark clouds. I smiled back - I couldn't help it - and he approached me. Then he reached out and touched the side of my head.

"I felt something like an electric shock. I blinked a couple of times, wondering if it was some kind of weird party trick: you know, a hidden induction coil or something. I was going to protest, then I suddenly realised something strange. My headache had gone, and the sick feeling with it. More than that, I felt incredibly well - better than I had felt in ages.

"Anyway, we introduced ourselves. He told me his name was Rami. He said he had been born with healing powers. I asked him if that was why he was so happy. 'Ah, Billy,' he replied. 'I have always been light of heart, but today of all days I have cause for rejoicing.'

"Well, naturally I was curious about that, so I asked him to explain. He told me that he had lived all his life in a remote hilltop village. Because of his powers, the village elders had told him that he must never, under any circumstance, unlock the door to the temple, or terrible things would befall him. That very day, he told me, he had finally succumbed to temptation, and opened the temple door for the first time."

"So why was he so happy?" Lisa asked.

Billy shrugged. "Probably because no terrible things happened."

Randy leaned forward. "But what did he actually SEE?"

"Well, that's the question." Billy beamed at them. "I'll bet you anything you want, you can't guess what he saw."

"Anything?" Mal asked incredulously. "Not just a beer or a burger?"

Billy's grin broadened still further. "Anything at all!"

Suddenly the room went quiet as everyone began thinking what the man could have seen to make him so happy.

All Billy's friends came up with plenty of suggestions for what Rami might have seen when he unlocked the temple door, but no one guessed correctly. Can you?

SOLUTION

Rami saw the outside world – because of his amazing healing powers, the elders in the village had locked him away in the temple since early childhood. They had kept him there by telling him that something awful would happen to him if he unlocked the temple door.

On the day Billy met him, Rami had unlocked the door from inside the temple (rather than outside) and looked out (rather than in).

The reason he was so happy was that a) he was free and b) nothing awful had happened to him.

14

SHIPWRECKED

SHIPWRECKED

The first thing Henry Johnson became aware of as he awoke was the warmth of the morning sun. The second was the not-so-distant lap of waves on the shore. And the third was a headache which felt as though someone was gouging out the inside of his skull with a chisel.

Blearily, Henry opened his eyes. He was lying on a sandy beach, about ten metres from the water's edge. He groaned as memory returned. Yesterday he had been sailing across the southern Pacific, blissfully alone. Then a dark cloud had appeared on the horizon. Quickly it had filled the sky and, as night fell, a tropical storm had broken around him. He had battled for hours to save his boat. He might have succeeded too, if it hadn't suddenly bucked on a huge wave, causing him to fall back and strike his head against the boom. Dazed, he lost his footing entirely, and slipped from the deck into the sea.

The storm had abated, but his boat was nowhere to be seen. Henry was cast adrift. His life-jacket kept him afloat, but the cold began to seep into his bones. His teeth chattered and he shivered uncontrollably. Eventually, though, the chill seemed to lessen. Lulled by the waves, he felt himself drifting into sleep - a sleep from which (a small part of him was anxiously aware) he would probably never awaken.

Then he was jerked back to full consciousness by his knee

scraping against a rock. He realised that the sea here was shallow, and when he looked up he could see a strip of white sand. On the horizon three tall palm trees were silhouetted against the moon. With the last vestiges of strength left in his limbs, Henry began to swim...

And now it was morning. Henry groaned again and sat up. Of his boat, 'The Happy Wanderer', there was no sign. The beach was deserted, and he realised the same was probably true of the whole island. There were no cigarette butts in the sand, no discarded cans, no mini-mopeds buzzing in the distance. It appeared that the tour operators had so far overlooked this particular jewel in the South Pacific.

The sun was getting hotter. Henry realised that, if he was to survive here, his first priority must be finding fresh water. He looked around. The palm trees he had seen last night were a little way inland; other than that, the island seemed to be mainly scrub. Rain was evidently a rare commodity here. Just my luck to be caught in their annual storm, he thought bitterly.

Henry rose unsteadily to his feet. He stripped off the heavy life jacket, so that he was just wearing cut-off jeans and a T-shirt, and headed towards the trees. His survival knowledge was limited, but he had an idea that their presence indicated fresh water nearby. He stumbled over the fine sand. Between the three palms, as he had hoped, there was a small pool. Henry cupped his hands and drank deeply. At least he would not die of thirst...not yet, anyway.

Henry's head was throbbing, and he realised he had to find some shade. He guessed the temperature to be into the nineties by now, although the sun was still nowhere near its zenith. He looked around. The island appeared flat and offered few possibilities, but further down the beach he could see a few pieces of driftwood. Perhaps they might form the basis of a shelter?

As Henry walked closer, he realised that they were parts of his boat. He even found a bit of the bow with the name 'The Happy Wanderer' on it, and some scraps of paper from his charts. His heart sank. Now he knew for sure that there would be no quick return to civilisation. He would have to wait to be rescued: possibly days, possibly weeks, possibly much longer.

Perspiring heavily, Henry gathered all the flotsam that he could find. As well as the wood and scraps of paper, he found a metal drinking mug, a tiny candle and a box of matches. The good news was that the latter had been wrapped in a plastic bag to keep out the damp; the bad news was that inside was only a single match. His most useful find, as far as shelter was concerned, was an oily tarpaulin. Returning to the palms, he built a sort of dug-out in the sand, which he covered with the tarpaulin. Luxury villa it wasn't, but at least it would give him some protection. He pulled himself inside and, exhausted, fell into a deep, dreamless sleep.

He was woken by a chill wind. The tarpaulin had blown off, revealing a clear, starry night, and had become caught on one of the palm trees, where it flapped loudly in the wind. Henry wrestled it back from the trunk. In that wind there was no chance of rebuilding his dug-out, so he wrapped the tarpaulin around himself to try to keep out the numbing cold.

Through the rest of the night, Henry slept little. His whole body ached; his head throbbed mercilessly; and his stomach growled, reminding him that he had not eaten for two whole days. He realised that he must have burned up a lot of energy fighting the storm and, later, in the sea. Unless he ate soon, he would become too weak to fend for himself.

The next day, fighting a growing lethargy, he managed to assemble what might be the makings of a meal. There wasn't much: just a few roots, some insect grubs, a yellow worm, and a small scorpion he had seen almost too late. But if he could start a fire, he might be able to make some kind of stew in the mug. Hands shaking, he collected together all the items he'd gathered from the wreck of his boat.

Henry paused, confused. His stomach was shrieking out for food, but his brain no longer seemed to be functioning correctly. He looked at the little collection in front of him - the scraps of wood he'd dried, the tiny candle and the scraps of paper from his charts - but he couldn't for the life of him figure out which to light first.

In order to light a fire, to cook the desperately needed meal, which of the items salvaged from the wreck of 'The Happy Wanderer' should Henry light first?

SOLUTION

He had no choice. The first
thing he would have to do is
light the match.

GOING
FOR GOLD

GOING FOR GOLD

Carla met Rodney while she was doing a postgraduate degree at Cornell University. She was studying the formation of atolls around the Pacific rim, and he was doing research for a doctorate in geology. They had met at a Christmas party that her professor was giving at the end of term. Carla had been bored and was about to leave when she saw Rodney walk in. He had a confident air about him and she felt a strong, overpowering attraction. She threw her coat across the arm of a sofa and went to get a beer out of the fridge.

Rodney was very friendly when she introduced herself and soon they were talking in an excited manner about their respective degrees. Carla told Rodney about her interest in the circular reefs formed by sunken volcanoes, and Rodney told her about his passion for what he called "the cooling rock". He told her about a grant he was applying for which would allow him to complete his thesis in Tahiti.

"Tahiti!" Carla exclaimed. "It's a dream of mine to go to Tahiti. It's a hot spot for atolls because of all the volcanic activity on the islands."

"If I get this grant," Rodney said, fuelled by alcohol and inspired by a growing sense of curiosity about the woman he was speaking to, "I'll take you with me."

"Is that a promise?" Carla asked.

Rodney put a hand over his heart and raised two fingers. "Scout's honour," he said then bent down and kissed her on the forehead.

Eight months later, Carla and Rodney were married; and in the Autumn of that year, they moved to Tahiti.

Carla and Rodney rented a small, secluded bungalow tucked away in the jungle at the foot of an extinct volcano. They would set out in the morning to climb to the top and gather lava samples, then Carla would lay out a lunch of sandwiches and fruit salad. On one of their excursions, they discovered a deep gorge with a river flowing through it not far from the house. They came across an old tattered rope bridge suspended eighty feet above the raging water.

"This must be the bridge the old man was telling me about," Rodney said.

"Oh, let's cross it," Carla pleaded.

"I can't," Rodney said. "I'm too heavy. Apparently the bridge can only hold a maximum of 125 lbs."

"I don't weigh that much," Carla said and stepped out onto the bridge.

"Please come back, Carla," Rodney pleaded. "You're making me nervous."

One day, a parcel arrived in the mail. It contained a letter from a solicitor informing Rodney that his father was dead. Carla was shocked.

"You told me your father died eight years ago," Carla said to Rodney.

"In a manner of speaking, he did," Rodney replied. "We fell out over money, which was typical because my father is a miser."

"Was a miser," Carla corrected him.

"We could have been very rich," Rodney said.

"What do you mean?"

"My parents had a lot of money," he explained. "When my mother died, I became the sole inheritor of my father's wealth. I was nineteen and in my first year at college. I was already studying geology. My father wanted me to give up my studies and work as an apprentice in his textiles factory. He wanted to pass on the business, but I refused. I had no interest in textiles, or working for my father for that matter. Things escalated, and we came to blows. That was the last time I saw him. The papers came later, but he legally disowned me."

"I can't believe you never mentioned this to me," Carla said and sat down. "Is that all the letter says?"

"No," Rodney said. "There's a receipt from the bank and a key. Something's been transferred to a safety deposit box here, but it doesn't say what it is."

That afternoon, Carla and Rodney went down to the bank and handed the slip to a teller. She escorted them into the safe and withdrew a long shallow box and handed it to Rodney. It was very heavy. Rodney looked at the bank teller and she excused herself so that they could be in private. Rodney placed the box on a shelf and inserted the key. He opened the lid and his eyes grew wide in amazement.

"What is it?" Carla asked.

Rodney withdrew two shiny gold ingots from the box and held them up for her to see. He turned them over in his hands. On the bottom was etched the weight of each bar of gold. They weighed nine pounds each.

Carla put the ingots in her bag. They thanked the bank teller and drove to their favourite restaurant. Rodney ordered a bottle of champagne and placed the two ingots on the table where he could get a better look at them. When the waiter glanced at the gleaming bars on the table, Rodney grabbed him by the arm and said, "Gold, man. It's pure gold."

The waiter was stunned. He asked if he could hold one, then he called the bartender over. Soon everybody at the restaurant had got up to take a look. Carla had never seen so many greedy eyes. She started to feel penned in by the crowd, unable to breathe. She wriggled out of her seat and pushed her way out of the circle of people that had gathered at their table. She went to the bathroom and splashed cold water on her face. This was bad news; she wished the letter had never arrived.

That night, Rodney and Carla had a fight. Rodney didn't feel like sleeping so he took the car and drove down to the ocean to walk along the beach. He was ashamed of his reaction to the gold, and the sea had always had a calming effect on him. He promised himself to take the ingots back to the bank the very next morning and sell them. He decided to donate half the money to an environmental charity, and put the rest into a separate account for when he and Carla had kids.

Back at the bungalow, Carla paced the porch waiting for Rodney to return. It had started to rain and Carla held her hand out to catch the cool drops in her palm. She felt nervous being left alone with the gold ingots and waited impatiently for her husband to come home.

While Carla was out on the front porch, two men broke into the house. They had heard about the gold from a friend who had been at the restaurant earlier that evening. They had been watching the house and seen the car speed down the driveway and figured that nobody was home. Carla jumped when she heard their voices, then crouched down under the living room window. She heard a man say, "Where do you think they put it?"

"How am I supposed to know?" another man answered.

"Try the bathroom," the first man said. "I'll check the bedroom."

Carla wanted to jump off the porch and run away, but then she remembered what Rodney had said earlier that evening. For the last year Carla had been wanting to get pregnant, but Rodney always said that they couldn't afford a baby. That night, he had agreed that now was a good time. Carla knew that the only reason he had said this was because of the gold, and she had become mad at him for being so materialistic. But now she understood why it was so important to him; the money would allow them to start a family. Suddenly the gold became very important to her too.

Carla crept back inside the bungalow and down the hall towards the kitchen. She had put the gold ingots back inside her bag after Rodney had stormed out, and left it on the kitchen table. Carla seized her bag and ran back down the hall towards the front door. As she passed the doorway to her bedroom, one of the robbers looked up and saw her.

"It's her!" he yelled. "Don't let her get away!"

Carla burst through the front door and out into the dark
night. She could hear the robbers close on her heels, yelling
and stumbling through the undergrowth. She found herself
running down the path towards the gorge and could hear the
river in the distance ahead of her. She needed a way to elude
the robbers and thought of the old rope bridge that crossed
the chasm. She remembered that the bridge could only
withstand a maximum of 125 lbs. She had weighed herself
recently and knew that she weighed 110 lbs.

When Carla got to the bridge, she stopped. The robbers were
quickly gaining on her. She took her shoes off, then rummaged
through her bag and withdrew the two gold ingots. She knew
they weighed 9 lbs each. She didn't want to part with them
but she couldn't carry both bars across at the same time or
the bridge would break. She realised that she didn't have
enough time to make two trips, and she couldn't throw the
bars because the ravine was too wide. Carla held her breath
and listened to the river roaring eighty feet below.

She looked back towards the jungle. She could just see the
two men emerging from the trees. Suddenly she had an idea;
it was easy after all. She was going to escape.

How did Carla manage to cross the gorge with both gold ingots?

SOLUTION

She walked across the
bridge, juggling the
ingots - so the weight
on the bridge was never
more than 119 lbs at
any one time.

GRETA AND THE GUNSLINGER

GRETA AND THE GUNSLINGER

The gunslinger swung down from his saddle and led his horse up the path towards a lone adobe hut. The moon was full and round in the black sky and it cast an eerie blue light on everything, as bright as if it were day. It was Monday night. The gunslinger knocked and waited.

A few minutes later, the door opened slowly and an old man emerged. He wore a red, woven, Mexican poncho over his grey long-johns, and he was holding a rifle.

"Well, I'll be," the old man said.

"Joshua," the gunslinger said, extending his hand. "I heard that my old home town was overrun by bandits, so I came back to volunteer my services."

"If anybody can bring peace to this God-forsaken town, you can. Come on in."

The gunslinger jangled into the house, all boot-spurs and ammunition, and sat down on a stool by the dying fire.

"I'll go get Edna to fix you some biscuits and gravy," the old man said and left the room.

When he returned, he had on his boots and a sheepskin coat. "I'll go unsaddle your horse. You just rest here for a while. It's been a long time, Howie, and I'm sure as hell pleased to see you."

"I'm still wanted in this county," the gunslinger said.

"The past is over and done with," the old man said. "What's more, Sheriff Watson was killed last week. A band of outlaws have taken over Winslow Town, and everybody's afraid."

"Don't be afraid, Joshua."

"To see you here, sitting in my house, I ain't got nothing to be afraid of no more."

On Tuesday morning, the gunslinger woke to the smell of freshly brewed coffee, pork rinds and buckwheat pancakes. Edna was warming syrup on the stove, humming softly to herself. The gunslinger sat up.

"I just can't get over it," Edna said. "Howie Sterne, we thought you were dead."

"Ain't dead till they bury me, Edna," he said and walked over to her and scooped her up by the waist.

"You put me down, Howie. I ain't a wee slip of a thing no more."

"But prettier for it," he answered.

"You always did know how to charm the womenfolk."

"And I aim to continue charming them till I got myself a wife. How's Greta?" he asked, giving Edna a wink.

Edna grew quiet and serious. "I guess you ain't heard."

"Heard what?"

"Greta's dead, Howie. She's buried next to her daddy in the Winslow cemetery."

"When did she die?" the gunslinger asked putting out his hand and steadying himself on the table.

"Sit down," Edna said, "and I'll tell you the whole story. You know how she was, stubborn as a mule, just like yourself, running the only hotel in town. When Grady and his men rode in on that fateful day and shot the mayor, well, the townsfolk just figured they'd run them out. But that proved impossible. Grady wanted to stay and some say it was because of Greta."

"Why?"

"Grady took one look at Greta and decided he wasn't going anywhere; not without her. For two months, Greta was forced to treat Grady and his men like paying customers, only they weren't paying, and soon Greta was running out of money. She told Grady he would have to leave, but that only made him want her all the more. Bill Benson, over at the dry goods store, said he heard shouting and screaming every night that week and then it stopped. Three days later, Grady opened the front door of the hotel and placed Greta's body on the porch."

"Had she been beaten?" the gunslinger asked.

"The coroner found traces of poison in her blood. He said it was suicide. They'd driven her to suicide!" Edna said and started to cry. "It's been terrible here. People are afraid to leave their homes. They're starving in their own kitchens. Oh, Howie, you've got to do something. Grady and his men are still holding the Baker sisters captive, Mary-Beth and Lola. The poor girls haven't been allowed to leave the hotel since the incident, and nobody dares set foot inside."

Two hours later, the gunslinger arrived at the Winslow cemetery. He left his horse at the gate and walked through the rows of rough-cut tombstones until he found the grave of

Ben Blacksmith. To the left was a new headstone, with a vase of wilted forget-me-nots under the name of Greta Blacksmith. The gunslinger removed his hat and knelt by the stone and traced the name with his fingers.

"Love of my life," he said gently to himself. "I will not forget."

The gunslinger spent that evening and the following day preparing to confront Grady and his men. He told Joshua to ride into the next county and purchase a case of bullets, a business suit and a bowler hat for him to wear. He made sure that his horse was well rested and in good condition. He ate a hearty meal and tried to sleep.

In the morning, the gunslinger strapped on all the ammunition he could carry under his new suit. He cut two holes in the sides of his jacket so he could reach his guns in a hurry. He slipped a small, loaded Remington into his boot, placed the bowler hat on his head, mounted his horse and, on Friday, rode into Winslow Town.

The streets were deserted. All the stores were boarded up and the swinging saloon doors were shut. There was no noise except the sound of the wind whistling down the barren main street. Somewhere a sign or a loose shutter creaked on its hinge. A sickly looking dog strayed out of an alley and sniffed the air. The gunslinger rode up to the Winslow Hotel and dismounted. He hitched his horse to the hitching post and walked the three steps up to the porch. He was greeted in the lobby by a very pale woman. She was wearing a threadbare dress that might have been regal once but now hung in tattered shreds off her thin and bony shoulders. Mary-Beth did not recognise the gunslinger.

"I'd like a room," he said.

"You don't want to stay here," Mary-Beth whispered.
"Please go away."

"Mary-Beth," he said. "It's me, Howie Sterne, the gunslinger."

"I thought you were dead," she answered.

"You mustn't tell anyone that I am here. Not even your sister,"
the gunslinger said. "Treat me like a stranger and give me
a room."

"Yes, sir," she said and turned and took a key off the shelf and
pointed him towards the stairs. "Room 103."

"Where's Grady?" the gunslinger asked.

"He's out just now but he's staying in room 104, across the
hall from yours," she answered.

"Much obliged," he said and made his way up the carpeted
staircase to room 103, to wait for Grady's return.

On Saturday night, there was a shoot-out at the Winslow
Hotel. The sound of gunfire could be heard for half a mile and
people from all over town came running out of their houses in
pyjamas, holding gas lamps and rifles. They began to gather
outside the hotel. They could hear shouts coming from inside
and see through the windows the dark silhouettes of men
running up and down the hall. After half an hour, Mary-Beth
stumbled out of the hotel dragging her injured sister, Lola,
and screaming for the doctor. A few minutes later, one of
Grady's men fell from a second-storey window. After him,

another man crept out onto the windowsill, trying to escape. He too was hit by a bullet and spun in the air before falling to his death.

Suddenly, the gunshots ceased. A strange hush fell over the town. Eventually the gunslinger emerged. He had blood on his face and shirt. His jacket was torn and a sleeve was missing. He raised his hand at the crowd and they waited for him to speak.

"Grady is dead," he said.

The crowd started to applaud. There were shouts of victory. Finally one man shouted, "Let's make Howie the new mayor." The crowd cheered their assent, but the gunslinger raised his hand again.

"I will be leaving tomorrow," he said. "My gunfighting days are over. All I want is a good night's rest." With that, the gunslinger turned and walked back into the hotel.

On Sunday morning, the gunslinger got up and went down to the lobby. Mary-Beth was sifting through the wreckage. He offered to pay his bill.

"I can't accept your money, Howie," she said.

"I insist," he replied. "You'll be needing it. What's the damage?"

Mary-Beth took out the ledger and wrote up a bill. She charged him for three nights.

Can you explain how the gunslinger rode into town on Friday, stayed three nights and left on Sunday morning?

SOLUTION

Friday was the name of his horse.
He had actually arrived at the
hotel on Thursday. He'd had to
wait two nights for Grady to
return on Saturday. Then he
stayed the third night after the
shoot-out and left on Sunday.

AROUND THE WORLD
IN SEVEN LIES

AROUND THE WORLD IN SEVEN LIES

As Chris Sanders left the office, he was surprised to see that it was almost dark. He glanced at his watch: eight o'clock. Time flies when you're busy, he thought. He'd been working late on his presentation for the Johnson pitch on Monday. Now it was done, and he was looking forward to going home and putting his feet up. His stride lengthened as he headed for the station.

"Chris, old man! Hang on!" Chris turned round. It was Jeremy Evershaw, whom he had first met at a clients' party three years ago. With his white suit and single gold earring, he had reminded Chris a little of Elvis in his Vegas days — apart from the fact that Jeremy, irritatingly, still had the physique of the younger Presley. Why Jeremy had made a bee-line for him, Chris didn't know. Perhaps he sensed a willing — or at least tolerant — listener for his travellers' tales. Their paths had crossed a few times since, though not for a year or so now.

Jeremy caught up with Chris and clapped him playfully on the back. "Working late on a Friday, old man? You'll never meet the love of your life that way, you know!"

Chris winced inwardly. During their first meeting he had let slip that he was divorced, and since then Jeremy had asked about his love life every time they met — while at the same time taking every opportunity to proclaim his own success with the ladies. "But of course, I play the field. Anyone can see that you're a one-woman man." And lucky if you can get that, his smirk implied.

Still, there was no denying Jeremy could be amusing company, and Chris had spent most of the day working on his own. He smiled. "What about you then, Jeremy? Don't tell me you were working late on a Friday?" Chris had never found out exactly what Jeremy did for a living, but judging by the stories he told, it must include a generous holiday allowance.

"Me? Not likely! Thought I'd go to a club, strut my stuff, then find a nice young lady and show her the constellations on my bedroom ceiling." Jeremy gave Chris a stage nudge. "But the night is young! Come on, let me buy you a drink. I've so much to tell you."

Chris hesitated. The image of his favourite armchair and a TV dinner swam enticingly in his mind, but with a conscious effort he blotted it out. What the hell, he thought. I've worked hard today and finished the presentation. I deserve a drink at least.

They walked the short distance to The Black Swan, a traditional pub serving a range of good ales, and found a quiet alcove. Jeremy bought the drinks — two pints of

Hook Norton Best — and settled himself comfortably on the upholstered bench seat. "Well, where do I start?" he grinned. "Only last week I got back from a safari holiday in Kenya."

"Kenya?" Chris said. "That must have been an experience."

"An experience? It was that all right! I stayed in a game lodge on the edge of the Masai Mara. We went out in Land Rovers in the morning, and again in the early evening."

"Did you see much?" Chris asked. "I've heard you see more tourists than wild animals on these trips."

"That may be so with some of the tourist outfits," Jeremy replied, "but the people I booked with were professionals. They knew all the best places to go, away from the crowds. I saw elephants, giraffes, rhinos, hippos, baboons and herds of antelope and zebra. One evening I even saw a lioness."

"Not bad," Chris had to admit. "What was the camp like?"

"The lodge, old man," Jeremy corrected. "It was everything you could wish for. I had a hut all to myself. And the food was splendid! The chefs cooked everything over an open fire, but the taste...well, you wouldn't believe you could eat so well, so far from civilisation."

Jeremy was getting into his stride by now. "And after dinner, around half-eight, we sat back and watched the local tribespeople performing their traditional dances, while the sun set slowly over the African plains. I tell you, Chris, it was heaven."

"It certainly sounds idyllic," Chris said. "A bit sedentary, though. Didn't you do anything more active – any walking or climbing, for instance?"

Jeremy was gazing over Chris's shoulder and didn't answer immediately. Glancing round, Chris saw that his attention had been drawn away by two young women, one blonde and one brunette, who had just entered the bar. The one with long blonde hair glanced briefly in their direction. Jeremy smiled back.

"Do you know those two?" Chris asked.

Jeremy's smile broadened. "Not yet. Now, what were you saying? Oh yes, climbing. Well, I did that all right. I didn't stay at the lodge the whole time I was in Kenya. In the last week of the holiday I decided it was time for a challenge, so I hired a local guide and headed for Mount Kilimanjaro."

Chris raised his eyebrows. "That's the highest mountain in Africa, isn't it?"

"It is. And I tell you, Chris, until you've stood on the summit and seen the great African plains spread out below you like a vast green tablecloth, you haven't lived." Jeremy took a long pull of his drink and set the empty glass down on the table. "Let me get you another."

"It's my round." Chris half-stood, but Jeremy put a restraining hand on his shoulder.

"I insist. Same again?" He strode towards the bar and positioned himself beside the young women. He murmured something to the blonde which made her companion giggle. The blonde said something back to Jeremy. The exchange might have continued, but the barman came to take Jeremy's order, during which time the women disappeared to a table on the other side of the room.

Jeremy came back, a slight smile on his face. "They like me," he said. "Or at least, they will when they get to know me." He put the beers on the table and sat down. "Anyway, speaking of travel, did I tell you about my plan to conquer Scandinavia?"

"Pardon me?" Jeremy's bragging was starting to irritate Chris, who had already spotted one or two inconsistencies in his story about Kenya.

"I'm planning to walk around Finland. Last Winter I did

Iceland, Norway, Sweden and Denmark. I had a few adventures on that trip, I can tell you."

And I'm sure you will, Chris thought. He smiled and sipped his beer. Taking this as an encouragement, Jeremy continued, "I started my journey in Iceland. Did you know the Arctic Circle runs right through the middle of the island, cutting it in two?"

Chris just shook his head.

"Well, anyway, you've heard of the hot springs? I came to this restaurant advertising 'Earth Cooking', and sure enough outside they had a cauldron hung over one of the springs — and in it was a steaming hot mushroom stew! So I stopped and had a bowl. It was delicious!"

"Did you enjoy all the walking?"

"Sure! I love walking. I did have one weird experience though. On the north of the island there are thousands of sea birds: puffins, penguins, gulls, Arctic terns and so on. Those terns are aggressive little beggars. They dive-bomb you like something from a Hitchcock film. I even pulled my hood right up over my head, but it didn't stop them. A couple of times they nearly ran me off course.

Chris was starting to find the one-sided nature of Jeremy's conversation oppressive. He decided to try a counter-offensive. "I've been invited to attend a conference in New York next month," he began, but Jeremy immediately interrupted him.

"New York, eh? Fancy you mentioning that! That's where I spent Easter this year. I had a great time. Don't forget to visit the Empire State Building, will you? There's an observation lounge on the hundred-and-second floor. On a clear day you can see up to eighty miles."

Chris sighed inwardly. He should have known better than to expect Jeremy to listen to anyone's stories but his own. "I'll bear it in mind," he said. "What else did you do while you were there?"

Jeremy beamed. "Well, being an old sea dog, I took a trip on the Staten Island Ferry. That's a great way to see the Statue of Liberty and the Manhattan skyline. I visited the Rockefeller Centre and Grant's Tomb. And I went to see the White House. You can't actually go in, of course, but even from the outside it's pretty impressive."

He took another pull of the Hook Norton. "Anyway, all this talk is making me peckish. I might just see what food's available here." Jeremy stood up and headed towards the servery. Chris suddenly noticed that there was a menu on the table. He was about to call Jeremy back, when he saw that the latter had veered to the left. Instead of going to the food hatch, he had pulled up a chair at the young women's table and begun chatting to them.

Chris looked away, embarrassed. The women would surely consider this harassment. Most likely they would call the manager and have them both thrown out. He opened his briefcase and took out a report. He pretended to study it, all the while expecting a heavy hand to descend on his shoulder. After about five minutes, however, nothing had happened. He risked a glance over to the young women, and was just in time to see the blonde passing a slip of paper to Jeremy. He grinned, and handed her what seemed to be a business card in exchange. "Catch you later," Chris heard him say, and watched as he sauntered back to the alcove.

"Thought you'd gone for some food?" Chris said. Half of him was amused, the other half – he had to admit – a bit envious.

Jeremy smiled. "I didn't see anything I fancied – not in the food line, at least."

Chris looked across at the young women, who were now engrossed in conversation. "What were you talking to them about?"

"The blonde girl – her name's Sian – told me she'd been to Greece this year. So I was telling them about my

Mediterranean cruise last Summer."

"Really," Chris said. "I don't think I heard about that one." Me and my big mouth, he thought instantly.

Jeremy leaned forward. "It was marvellous, old man. I travelled first class on a luxury liner, stopping off at Corsica, Alexandria, Port Said, Tenerife, Rhodes, Santorini...so many wonderful Mediterranean ports of call."

"What did you do on board?" Chris asked. "I've heard all there is to do on a cruise is eat."

"Well, the food was five-star, of course. But you know me, Chris..." Jeremy patted his flat stomach complacently, "...I like to keep in shape. So I did plenty of things to keep fit. During the day I headed for the ship's gym, and at night I went running."

"On board a ship?" Chris shook his head wonderingly. "Where did you run?"

"I must have covered every inch of the ship's floor. I ran from the front to the back, the left to the right, pounding those boards. Some of the other passengers thought I was mad, but it paid off. One evening I was invited to the Captain's table and sat next to this stunning Italian heiress. Well, I could see at once that she was attracted to me, but I thought, take your time,

Jeremy, play it cool. So I did, at first. But later that night...well, delicacy forbids, of course, but..."

By now Chris had heard enough. He stood up. "Jeremy," he said, "I've listened to you all evening, and I know for sure now that you're a liar. Thanks for the drinks, but I don't want to listen to any more of your tall tales." As he opened the door he glanced back, and noted with satisfaction that his erstwhile drinking companion was still sitting there, eyes wide and mouth open.

For probably the first time in his life, Jeremy Evershaw was lost for words.

Chris was right to call Jeremy a liar, and he has seven bits of information gleaned from their conversation to verify his claim. What are they?

SOLUTION

The seven pieces of information are:

1. On Jeremy's trip to Kenya he claimed to have watched the sun set at half-past eight in the evening yet Kenya is near the equator, so the sun always sets there at around 6pm.

2. Also in Kenya, he said he climbed Mount Kilimanjaro but Kilimanjaro is in Tanzania.

3. The Arctic Circle does not bisect Iceland, it passes just to the north of it.

4. While walking in Iceland, he claimed to have seen penguins, which are found only in the Antarctic.

5. In New York, he claimed to have visited the White House, which is in Washington DC.

6. On his Mediterranean cruise, the stop-overs Jeremy mentioned included Tenerife, which is in the Atlantic, not the Mediterranean.

7. Jeremy claimed to be an 'old sea dog', yet he referred to the floor of the ship rather than the deck, the ship's back and front rather than its bow and stern, and left and right rather than port and starboard. No former sailor would describe a ship in such terms.

BRIDGING
THE GAP

BRIDGING THE GAP

Scott Mercy was a major in the Sherwood Rangers Regiment of the British Army, which had been chosen to do a tour of duty in Bosnia, under the overall control of the United Nations. His duties in Bosnia included the supervision of food distribution, the protection of the local civilian population and all administrative and communicative installations, that is, airports, roads, bridges, telegram offices, etc.

On the first day of his new assignment, Major Mercy chose four men from the platoon to form a small mobile unit to serve as scouts. Whenever Mercy received a transmission that a hospital had been bombed, or that a bridge or a road was down, he sent these four men ahead to assess the situation. When he heard that a bridge on the road from Plehan to Sarajevo had been hit, he sent his scouts out immediately to lay new cables to rebuild the bridge. It was imperative that the bridge be fixed because the road served as a main artery, along which the UN was scheduled, in twenty-four hours, to deliver emergency medical supplies to the devastated city of Sarajevo.

That evening Mercy received a transmission from the mobile unit. It was Private Kenning on the radio and the line was bad.

"Sir," he said. "It's worse than we anticipated. The river is swollen because of the rain. It's thick with mud and there's no way we can get across. The banks are crumbling and won't support the weight of our vehicles. We can't get close enough to lay the cables. Over."

"How bad's the bridge?" the major asked. "Over."

"There's no sign of the bridge. The river swallowed it up. Over."

"Any gunfire?" the major asked. "Over."

"It's pretty quiet here, sir. We can see civilians on the other side, but we can't get to them. Over."

"Stay put and keep the line open. I'm coming down in the armoured jeep. Over and out."

Private Kenning handed the radio back to Private Lister and informed his unit that the major was on his way. They stood around smoking cigarettes and watching the river rush downstream. A young sapling that had been growing along the river bank, suddenly became dislodged and sunk into the brown water. It popped to the surface and was carried swiftly along by the current. Private Cross, jokingly referred to by his buddies as Robin Hood, because of his expertise in archery, shook his head, sat down on a rock in the shelter of a spruce tree, took out his army knife and started to whittle away at a long thin branch. Private Handy also sat down, pulled his blue beret down over his eyes and tried to sleep. Kenning looked up at the bleak sky and listened to the rain fall on the shoulders of his white, army-issue poncho. Night was falling and the cold had begun to seep through to his skin. He shivered.

Back at camp, the major summoned his driver and gave him orders to transport him to the bridge. They climbed into the white, armoured jeep, with the blue UN flag flapping at the end of a long antenna, and started down the rain-soaked road towards the river. When they were still twelve miles from the bridge, the jeep slid sideways in the mud and into a ditch. The major got out and piled rocks in front of the rear tyres to give the vehicle some purchase, but when the driver put the jeep in gear and inched forward, the rocks simply sunk deeper into the mud. The driver tried rocking the jeep back and forth while the major pushed, but for all their efforts, the thing wouldn't budge.

"Looks like we're stuck, sir," the driver said.

"It's getting dark," replied the major. "It'll be curfew time soon and we'll be cut off. Hand me the radio."

The major called ahead to the mobile unit and informed Private Kenning that he would not be able to reach them in time. "I'm leaving the situation up to you boys. Somehow you've got to figure out how to lay the cables across the river by morning. I'll make sure the rest of the platoon arrives at 08:00 hours. In the meantime, you get those cables across. People's lives depend on it."

"Yes, sir," Kenning said and put the radio down. He told the unit to listen up and informed them of the situation.

"What are we supposed to do?" Lister asked. "Swim across?"

"That would be impossible," Kenning said.

"What about making a raft?" Handy suggested.

"Nice one," Kenning said. "But have you happened to notice the current of the water? You'd be swept away in seconds. You'd be in the heart of Sarajevo in five minutes. How would you like that?"

"OK, forget it," Handy said.

"What about a helicopter?" Lister said. "We could radio the major and request permission."

Kenning checked his watch and said, "Curfew started five

minutes ago. Any helicopter that's still in the air is fair game. It would get shot down before it even had a chance to get here. That's not an option."

The men fell silent, each one racking his brain to find a solution.

"What about you, Cross?" Kenning asked. "You've been mighty quiet. We're trying to help the war effort here. If we don't get these cables laid by 08:00 hours, there are women and children who aren't going to get the medical attention they need in time, and will die."

"Calm down," Cross said with a wry smile. "I've got an idea. You know how to speak the language fluently, don't you Kenning?"

"That's right," Kenning answered.

"You still carrying that megaphone around, Lister?"

"I sure am. It's in the jeep."

"Good. Now can you shine the headlights in the direction of those civilians on the other side?"

"No problem."

"What's this all about?" asked Kenning.

"Let me explain..."

By 08:00 hours the following morning, the rain had stopped, the cables were laid, and major Mercy's platoon was able to build the new bridge.

What was the idea which Private Cross had and how were the four scouts able to lay the cables across the river before their 08:00 deadline?

53

SOLUTION

With the help of the loud speaker, Kenning asked the civilians on the other side of the river to help them. Then Cross, who was an expert archer and was able to fashion a bow and arrow out of some branches, fired an arrow, with a string attached, across to the other side of the river. The scouts had kept hold of one end of the string and, in the light from the jeep's headlights, the civilians were able to find the arrow and pull the string. After a while, the scouts attached heavier ropes to the string and eventually the cables were attached and pulled across the river by the helpful civilians.

54

THE GOLD PENDANT

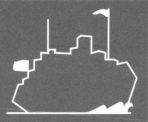

THE GOLD PENDANT

Professor Ryan Ironside had spent the last five years of his life pin-pointing the exact location of the Lost City of the Incas. He had spent so much time in Peru that he no longer felt that he had any ties with the State of Virginia, where he was from. His mother had given up the hope of ever seeing him again, and her letters pleading him to come home came less frequently now.

Ryan Ironside lived alone in a bamboo hut and owned the only generator in the village, which he had bought with a grant from the University of Baltimore. Every night, as Ryan and his archaeological assistant, Bartholomew Tool, pored over ancient maps and parchments, the children from the village would gather at the window like moths, attracted by the electric light.

Ryan had befriended one child in particular, an eight-year-old boy by the name of Gabriel Thuente, who had stuck to him like a shadow for the first six months. Eventually, Ryan employed the boy for his uncanny knowledge of the surrounding area. Burdened with equipment, Gabriel would clamber through the dense rainforest and lead Ryan and Bartholomew right to the spot they had marked on the map. Gabriel would then sit back on his haunches and watch the two archaeologists clear the underbrush and mark the area with stakes and lengths of twine, then meticulously sweep the soil layer by layer into flat, round sifting trays.

Five years after his arrival in the village, Ryan had a

breakthrough. It was a hot and humid afternoon and he and Bartholomew were excavating a site high up in the Andes. The air was thin and Ryan was dizzy and tired. He was scraping at the dry soil with a pick when he hit something solid, like rock or clay. He dusted the area with his brush and uncovered what looked like a wall. He sat up and called Bartholomew over.

"It's a miracle," Ryan said. "This is what we've been waiting for. Look how straight the bricks are laid. It's a perfect structure. Gabriel, bring me my twelve-inch trowel."

Gabriel, who was thirteen years old by this time, rushed over with some more equipment and the three of them began digging and brushing the earth aside until they had uncovered the top inch of the entire rectangular structure.

"It's a house!" Gabriel shouted.

"It's too small to be a house," Bartholomew said.

"It's a sepulchre," Ryan said. "A very elaborate Inca burial chamber."

Gabriel crossed himself and took a few steps backwards, murmuring a prayer under his breath. "It is bad luck," he said, "for the first man to uncover it. It is like a curse, Mr Ironside. I will pray for your soul."

"You don't believe all that mumbo-jumbo, do you, Gabriel?"

"With a find like this, I'm going to be famous," Bartholomew said quietly to himself.

"Forget fame for the moment," Ryan said. "It's nearly dark. We've got work to do."

After six months of back-breaking work, of identifying and labelling every fragment they found, Ryan and his colleagues uncovered a small skeleton lying at the bottom of the tomb. The skeleton was that of a young woman, no older than fourteen years old when she died. Around her neck were the tarnished remains of a gold pendant, on which were engraved ancient geometric designs.

Ryan wrote up a report and sent it to the archaeology department of the University of Baltimore and his findings were published in the September edition of The American Archaeology Journal. After that, the site was overrun with experts and Ryan and his colleagues retreated back down the mountain to the village.

The only thing that Ryan had not reported was the existence of the gold pendant. Bartholomew and Gabriel had agreed to keep it a secret until they had had a chance to decipher the riddle on the pendant. The skeleton was believed to be the remains of the second child-bride of the last Inca Sun King, Atahuallpa, who was mythologically descended from Manco Capac, High Priest of the Sun. Atahuallpa was later murdered by the Spaniards in 1533, but was reputed to have given each of his brides the key to the Lost City of the Incas.

Ryan believed that the mysterious symbols on the pendant formed a map that, if he could decipher it, would lead him straight to the legendary city. He felt that he was on the brink of proving its existence to the world and, after dedicating his life to the task, he was not about to let anyone steal his fire.

Ryan and Bartholomew closed up the bamboo hut, turned off the generator and drove to the capital city of Lima. They spent two months in the Lima City Archives researching the ancient language of the Incas. They took notes on the meaning of certain geometric patterns, including primitive drawings of birds and fish, the sun and stars. Loaded down with journals and files, they finally returned to the village where they were warmly greeted by Gabriel and his family. Gabriel's mother had cooked a huge feast and, that night, they dined with the Thuente family.

Across the dinner table, Gabriel asked Ryan many questions about his research. Ryan spoke freely, knowing that Gabriel's family could not understand what he was saying. He told Gabriel that they were very close; that there were only two more symbols left to interpret before the riddle unfolded itself. Gabriel's eyes lit up and he put his hand on Ryan's arm.

"We have come so far," Gabriel said. "Nothing can stop us now."

"Nothing but our own ignorance," Bartholomew said.

"You are always so pessimistic," Gabriel told him. "You need more faith."

"I cannot take advice from a thirteen-year-old boy," Bartholomew answered.

"He's just jealous," Ryan said to Gabriel.

"Jealous of what?" Bartholomew asked.

"I saw the letter you wrote to your father," Ryan said. "It was on the table at the hotel. You told him that you hated the way I took charge; the way this was my project. But let me remind you, I took you on in the beginning as my assistant. This was my passion to begin with. You wouldn't be here if it wasn't for me."

"You don't have to remind me," Bartholomew said and got up from the table.

"Where are you going?"

"I'm going out," he answered and left the table.

"Let him go," Gabriel said and consoled his mother in Spanish. "Have some more food."

Ryan helped himself to some more beans. He picked up the small clay bowl of salt and sprinkled a pinch over his plate. Then he did the same with the pepper. As he was rubbing the pepper between his fingers it came to him, in a flash, like lightning to his brain - an electrical current - and he stood up, knocking his chair backwards.

"That's it!" he exclaimed, pulling Gabriel up from his chair and swinging him around the room.

"What? What?" Gabriel shouted.

"Salt and pepper!" Ryan shouted. "Salt and pepper! The high priest of the sun had two mythological brothers! What were their names?"

"Cachi and Uchu," Gabriel said. "Everybody knows that."

"Do you know what those names mean in English?"

"I've never thought about it," answered Gabriel.

"Salt and pepper! Those are the last two symbols. Salt

and pepper!"

That night Ryan and Gabriel stayed up, studying the riddle under the glare of a bare light bulb. The village was silent. By three-thirty in the morning, they had solved the riddle. It was all written down plainly on a sheet of paper. They located a rough site on the map and promised each other to go there the following morning. They parted company and Ryan sat down on his bed.

He was still so wide awake. He undressed and lay down. He stared out of the window at the stars humming in the firmament. Tomorrow he would come in contact with ancient history, the sun-worshippers, people who were long dead, people who had at one time stared at the same stars as he did now, people who did not know that stars were suns in their own right. What would they have done if they had known that? They would have had a countless number of gods...

Ryan woke up to a pounding at the door.

"Wake up, Mr Ironside. It's time to go find the Lost City of the Incas!"

"Coming, Gabriel," Ryan said and flung back the sheets.

As Ryan was crossing the room to the door, he noticed that the table was empty. There was nothing on it. The notes they had made the night before were gone. Ryan opened the door and looked at Gabriel.

"You look like you have seen a ghost," Gabriel said.

"The notes, the map, it's all gone."

"Gone?" Gabriel exclaimed. "How, gone?"

"Bartholomew," Ryan answered soberly.

"That traitor!" Gabriel shouted. "We've got to stop him!"

"But how?"

"He can't have gone far. I know the roads. I will ask my uncle. He works on the toll-bridge. Nobody gets by him."

Ryan and Gabriel jumped into the jeep and set off down the muddy road. They reached the toll-bridge that crossed a canyon on the way down the mountain. Gabriel got out and ran into the toll booth. He returned with his uncle who was gesticulating furiously - Bartholomew hadn't even stopped to pay the toll, but had driven right through the barrier. Ryan looked to his left and saw the broken plank of wood. He reached into his pocket and pulled out some money. He handed Gabriel's uncle fifty dollars.

"For repairs," he said. "Let's go. Thanks for your help."

Gabriel got back into the jeep and they sped down the winding road that led to the coastline.

"I bet he's headed for the ferry," Gabriel said. "We have to reach him before he gets to the boat."

Ryan drove quickly and skilfully and an hour later, they had reached the coastal city of Arequipa. The streets were crowded with people. Ryan honked the horn and tried to get through, but was forced to slow down to a walking pace.

"It would be faster to run," Gabriel said. "I know a short cut down to the port."

They left the jeep in the middle of the road and ran through the streets.

"Through here," Gabriel called and pointed down a dark, narrow passageway.

They emerged into the market place and Ryan caught a glimpse of the sea in front of him. He heard the drone of a ship's horn and then, in the distance, he caught sight of Bartholomew. He shouted and ran towards him. Bartholomew saw him and raced down to the docks. There was a boat about twelve feet beyond the pier, moving swiftly through the water.

Bartholomew knew this was his only chance of escape. He tucked his briefcase into his shirt and ran after the boat. He aimed and leaped off the dock and just managed to grab hold of the railing. He pulled himself onto the deck and lay on his side for a moment. His leg was throbbing. He thought he might have broken his ankle, but he had managed to get away.

A smile broke out on his face. He saw Ryan and Gabriel waving madly on the pier, shouting at him as the boat sliced through the water. He had got his revenge and, for a short, sweet moment, he felt the thrill of victory. He would be famous, after all.

Suddenly, he felt a hand on his shoulder and turned to face a deckhand in a white shirt and khaki shorts. The deckhand asked him a question. Bartholomew stopped smiling and his face turned pale. He started to cry.

What on earth could the deckhand have asked Bartholomew to react in this way?

SOLUTION

The deckhand had asked Bartholomew why he had risked his life by jumping on board the moving ferry when it was minutes away from mooring - ie he'd told Bartholomew that the boat was just coming into the port, not leaving it!

64

DEATH ON
KILIMANJARO

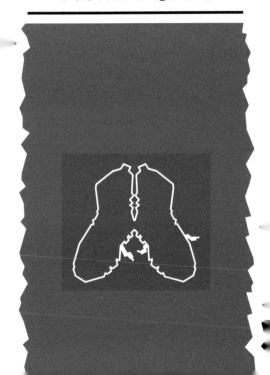

DEATH ON KILIMANJARO

For at least the tenth time that day, Kurt was vanishing out of sight. "For Chrissake, Kurt, slow down!" Joey shouted.

Ahead of him on the narrow track, Kurt paused in his stride. He turned, lip curled in an expression of contempt. "Can't hack it, Joey? You go back if you want. I'm heading for the summit."

"I don't want to turn back. I just gotta...get my breath." Joey felt suddenly dizzy. He sank to his knees. Kurt looked on, making no attempt to help.

"Great adventurer," he said, making it sound like an obscenity. "I always knew you were a loser, Joey. Can't even make it up Kilimanjaro. It's barely six thousand metres. Nothing to an experienced mountaineer."

Like you, I suppose, Joey thought sardonically, but he didn't have the strength to argue. He had quickly realised that Kurt had never climbed a mountain in his life. He had approached this whole project like a Sunday afternoon stroll. Yet so far, anyway, he seemed immune to the altitude sickness that befell almost anyone who tried to climb too quickly. Feeling sick, Joey groped in his jacket pocket for his Diamox tablets.

Kurt reached into his pocket as well. He took out a cigarette. "I'll smoke this, Joey boy, then I'm going on. You can come with me, or you can head back. It's your choice."

It had all been very different two days ago when they had arrived in Tanzania. Although hot and tired from their long journey, they had both been full of excitement at the prospect of the adventure ahead. They spent their first night at the Hotel

Marangu, a faded but still-elegant establishment which was presided over by two matronly Englishwomen. Over a meal of 'Chicken Marangu', they planned their assault on the mountain.

"Of course, most first-timers take the tourist trail," Joey pondered. "But that's the least scenic route..."

"Tourist trail?" Kurt slammed his glass down on the table, spilling his Pilsner beer. "Don't make me laugh, Joey. We're adventurers, for God's sake, not tourists! We take the toughest route available!"

They settled on the Machame Trail. It wasn't actually the toughest, but privately Joey figured it would be more than challenging. The hotel owners arranged climbing permits and the hire of a jeep. They also provided trail maps, and recommended the services of two local porters. Kurt wasn't having that, though.

"Porters are for train stations," he said. The older woman peered at him over her lorgnette. She pursed her lips, but said nothing.

Once the necessary arrangements had been made, they journeyed by jeep to the base of Africa's highest mountain. The road wound through coffee fields and small forests of ferns and flowers. The heat was stifling, and Joey was glad when they reached their destination and could at last get out of the vehicle. They parked beside two other off-roaders and strapped on their rucksacks. Then, watched by a chattering tribe of tree monkeys, they began the hot and dusty five-hour trek through the forest to Machame Hut, where they had arranged to spend the night.

The next day the climb began in earnest. Leaving the hut early in order to make good progress before the sun grew too strong, they crossed a small valley, covered with exotic Spring flowers. Then the landscape changed from forest to scrubland, littered with wild cactus plants. They crossed a river gorge and arrived, according to the map, at the Shira Plateau. The heat was intense, and on top of it Joey had a splitting headache. He knew it to be the first symptom of altitude sickness. More symptoms had swiftly followed.

Kurt finished his cigarette and ground it under his heel. He stared at Joey. "Well?"

Joey climbed to his feet. He took a deep breath and exhaled slowly. He still felt lousy, but his head had cleared. The Diamox had done its work...this time, anyway. "I'm all right," he said. "Let's take it steady, shall we?"

They climbed on, up the track that led to the summit. Joey still felt pretty wasted, but thought he might just manage this last stretch, as long as they could descend straight afterwards. Kurt stopped suddenly. "Look," he said.

Joey followed his pointing arm. Some way below, two other climbers were making their way down the mountain on another trail. One looked up and waved. At this distance, it was hard to tell whether it was a man or a woman. Joey watched till they disappeared behind some rocks.

"Looks like they made it," Joey said. "That'll be us in a few..." He stopped, staring at his partner.

Kurt was panting heavily. His face was covered in beads of sweat. "What are you looking at?" he snarled. He turned and took a few steps, then stumbled and fell. His rucksack flew open, scattering clothing and utensils. Joey rushed over to him.

Kurt lay on his back, mouth open. "My chest!" He gasped like a fish out of water. "Oh God, Joey, it feels like it's being crushed."

Joey didn't like this at all. This was more than plain altitude sickness. He tried to remember what the book had said about High Altitude Pulmonary Oedema. He was positive the crushed chest sensation was a sign. Fluid was building up in Kurt's lungs. Unless he got back to lower altitudes quickly, death would most certainly follow. They had to return to the hut where they had stayed last night. But there was no way that Joey could, in his present state, get Kurt back there on his own.

"I'll get help," he said. Kurt, still gasping, didn't reply. Joey went back to the place where they had watched the other climbers descending; however, by now, there was no sign of them. He walked on a little way, shouting, but there was no reply. He hurried back to check on Kurt who was, by now, unconscious. His own heart pounding, Joey felt Kurt's wrist. There was still a faint pulse.

There was no alternative. Quickly, Joey located and launched their emergency flare. There was a loud report as it erupted in a ball of magnesium light that momentarily rivalled the African sun.

Although others saw the emergency signal, they were unable to help and within two minutes of launching the flare, both Kurt and Joey were dead. Why?

SOLUTION

The flare set off an
avalanche which killed the
two men. Although it is hot
on the lower slopes of
Kilimanjaro, the peak is
always covered in snow.

HIGHLY STRUNG

HIGHLY STRUNG

A lfonzo the Magnificent bowed to the audience. He put his hands into the bowl of chalk and clapped them together. The band stopped playing and the drum-roll began. All the spotlights were fixed on Alfonzo as he began to climb the ladder up to the platform thirty feet in the air.

Waiting for him at the top of the ladder was his beautiful assistant, Clara, dressed in a pink bodysuit and wearing a crown of white ostrich feathers. When he stepped onto the platform, she handed him the balancing pole. The drum-roll ceased and a hush fell over the crowd. The air was hot and humid at the top of the circus tent, and Alfonzo gave Clara the signal to wipe his brow with a lace handkerchief. She then dangled the handkerchief in mid-air, at the end of her long, outstretched fingers and let it drop slowly to the ground. There was no safety net to catch the flimsy, white square as it floated down to the ring below, and people shifted nervously in their seats, craning to get a better look at the little man in the black tuxedo perched like a penguin in the sky.

The circus master tapped the end of his microphone and circled the ring, flicking the electrical cord like a whip. "Tonight, ladies and gentlemen, Alfonzo the Magnificent, tightrope walker extraordinaire, will perform a death-defying feat. There is no safety net to catch him if he falls, so I urge the audience to remain quiet throughout, and please refrain from taking any pictures as the flash might distract our performer. Good luck, Alfonzo. Now on with the show!"

Alfonzo looked straight ahead. He slid a slippered foot onto the wire and adjusted the pole in his hands. He slid his other foot out and steadied himself. He slowly raised his left foot and circled it around his right, then slid it forward. He heard a man cough in the darkness below him, but continued to stare straight ahead. When Alfonzo reached the centre of the wire, he stopped. He raised himself onto the balls of his feet, threw his pole into the air and the crowd gasped. Alfonzo spun around, then caught the pole again. He teetered to one side, tottered to the other, while the audience below oohed and aahed. He managed to stabilise himself and continued on towards the other platform. When he reached it, there was an explosion of cheering and whistling. Sweat broke out on Alfonzo's forehead as he raised his hand in the air and bowed again with a flourish.

After the performance, as Alfonzo was wiping his make-up off, his old rival, Guiseppe, burst into the dressing room.

"So you think you are the best tightrope walker in the whole of Argentina?" Guiseppe said.

"Well, they don't call me Alfonzo the Magnificent for nothing," Alfonzo replied. "I know how to please a crowd. It is I they want, not some third-rate amateur like yourself."

"I am not here for insults, Alfonzo. I came here to challenge you to the tightrope duel of your life. I dare you to meet me at the Plaza Maria on Thursday week, at midnight, where we will judge, once and for all, who is the best."

"I am the best!" Alfonzo cried. "I am the best in Buenos Aires, the best in Argentina and perhaps even the best in the world!"

"Then prove it," Guiseppe said, slamming the door on his way out.

Nine days later, Alfonzo looked at himself in the mirror and adjusted his bow tie. It was eleven o'clock on Thursday night, one hour before the duel. He picked up his pole and his bucket of chalk and headed for the door. He felt a slight foreboding but chose to ignore it.

As he approached the Plaza Maria, he could hear the crowd that had gathered to watch. He turned a corner and saw the plaza at the far end of the street. There were lights strung up between the buildings, and high above the square, Alfonzo saw the silver wire gleaming like a blade between the cathedral spire and the balcony of the Italian Embassy building. In the centre of the plaza, a man on a unicycle was juggling tenpins. As he got closer, he saw a woman with a snake wrapped around her shoulders.

When Guiseppe arrived, they tossed a coin to see who would go first. It landed heads up, and Alfonzo prepared himself to climb the ladder. He dusted his hands, and looped the pole through his belt at the small of his back. He took one step and paused, then continued his ascent. The wire was a hundred feet up in the air and it took Alfonzo five and a half minutes to reach the top. When he stepped onto the slanted roof of the cathedral spire, he noticed a chill in the air. He could not hear the crowd for the wind in his ears.

From the ground, Guiseppe watched Alfonzo pull the pole out from under his belt and lay it across his hands. Alfonzo waited for a moment and then slid one foot out onto the wire. Just as he was about to lift his other foot, his body jerked and the pole slid through his hands. He bent to retrieve it but it was too late. It had started to slide down the roof. It slipped off the edge and fell down into the crowd. Alfonzo turned and started back down the ladder.

When he got to the bottom, Guiseppe was waiting for him.

"What on earth are you doing?" he screamed.

"I can't go on like this," Alfonzo said, pushing Guiseppe aside and striding off through the plaza and down a main street. Guiseppe set off after him.

Alfonzo stopped in front of the entrance to a bar and looked up at the sign. The bar belonged to a friend of his, and he opened the door and walked in. He walked over to the counter and ordered a glass of water. The bartender smiled knowingly at him, took a revolver out from under the bar and shot a bullet into the ceiling. After waiting a few moments, Alfonzo thanked his friend and they shook hands. He turned and left the bar without taking a sip of his water.

Why did the bartender shoot the ceiling, and why did Alfonzo thank him?

SOLUTION

Alfonzo had hiccups and knew he could not perform on the tightrope without getting rid of them. The bartender had realised he had hiccups and had successfully got rid of them by firing the gun thereby giving him a fright, which is a much more effective cure than drinking water.

THE LOST IDOL

THE LOST IDOL

Savage was late. Raybould sipped the last of his Black Russian. He would give the man five more minutes, then depart. He had better things to do than sit in the bar of Grant's restaurant waiting for some young chancer who couldn't read a watch.

Two more minutes passed, then the door from the street opened and a man with close-cropped, almost white hair and striking, pale blue eyes emerged into the foyer. He looked around, a faint smile playing over his lips. Raybould recognised Mark Savage at once from the photo he had sent. He raised a hand to draw his attention.

"Mr Raybould?"

"Mr Savage. You know you are over an hour late?"

"I'm sorry." The man had a surprisingly deep, mellifluous voice. "I was researching in the library and lost track of time."

"I trust you have no objection to dining straight away?"

"Of course not."

Raybould stood. He nodded to the waiter who had appeared discreetly at the door to the restaurant. "Evening, Andre."

"Good evening, Monsieur Raybould. Your usual table is ready for you."

Grant's restaurant was large and genuinely old, with low ceilings and thick oak beams. As well as the main dining area, which was about half-full, there were a number of smaller rooms leading off. Raybould's table was in an alcove in one of these. Privacy was guaranteed by thick drapes on three sides, and a curtain that could be pulled on the fourth.

Andre handed them two leather-bound menus. "An aperitif, Monsieur Raybould?"

"Have you any more of that excellent sherry - the Amontillado?"

"Bien sûr, monsieur. And for your guest?"

"Whatever," Savage said airily. Raybould frowned. Clearly this young man had little appreciation of the finer things. Still, no doubt he had more pressing concerns. Well, no time like the present, he thought.

"So, Mr Savage, perhaps you'd like to explain your proposition, and how it may be worth five million pounds to me."

"Certainly." Savage looked relieved to be getting down to business. "Three years ago I was on a trekking holiday in Peru. A friend had told me about the Inca Trail, and I decided I must see it for myself. The trail follows the ancient road that originally linked Cuzco and Machu Picchu, the mysterious ruined city of the Incas."

Andre arrived with the sherries. Savage remained silent till he had left, then he pulled the curtain shut. He took a large swig of sherry, then continued: "I followed the trail from Huayllabamba to Dead Woman Pass, and onward into the jungle. And it was there, near an Inca ruin called Sayacmarca, that I was taken captive." Savage paused dramatically, but the effect was marred by a cough from outside the alcove. Raybould pulled back the curtain.

"You are ready to order, Monsieur Raybould?"

"I am. Mr Savage?"

Savage stood up suddenly. "I must make a call," he said. "Would you order for me?"

Raybould watched quizzically as Savage strode back to the foyer. He turned to Andre. "Young people today - always in such a rush. I'll have your excellent brazil and cashew nut roast with chestnut stuffing and red wine sauce, accompanied by potato galette with baby vegetables."

"Oui, monsieur. And for your guest?"

Raybould shrugged. "The same. And a bottle of your best Montrachet, please."

Andre nodded and departed. Raybould smiled to himself. He hoped Savage enjoyed vegetarian food. Though on the evidence so far, Raybould wondered if he would even notice.

Some ten minutes passed before Savage returned. Seated again, he resumed his story. "I was alone in the ruins as night fell. Suddenly I was surrounded by six native tribesmen, naked apart from daubings on the face and body. Their leader indicated that I should go with them, and I wasn't going to argue; they carried stone knives and axes which looked as though they could cause serious damage.

"We walked by moonlight for what seemed like hours. I was pretty shaken, of course, but I kept a mental note of our

80

route. Though I say it myself, I have a good sense of direction. We eventually arrived at their village, deep in the heart of the jungle."

Just then Andre arrived with the food. The aroma was delectable, and Raybould paused to savour it. Savage, however, simply piled in, filling his fork and shovelling the fine ingredients down. If he noticed the absence of meat, he made no mention.

"Anyway," he said, through a mouthful of potato, "I found out the tribe was called the Araka. They had no contact with civilisation, and their elders had made the decision to capture one of these strangers who passed through their territory, I suppose to find out what made us tick. They kept me prisoner in a hut which was guarded at all times."

Savage paused to cram more food into his mouth, then continued: "I was fed on a diet of nuts and berries. I must have lost about forty pounds in weight. But I survived, and after a while I began to take an interest in their customs and - in particular - their religion. Opposite my hut, you see, was a much grander one which I realised was their temple. Whatever was inside, the tribesmen treated it with the deepest respect.

"I found out the Araka worshipped a god called Manco Capac. Now, I'd done a bit of reading, and I knew that Manco Capac was the son of Inti, the Inca Sun God. The ancient records mentioned a fabulous golden statue of Manco Capac, but it was believed to be lost forever. Now, just possibly, I realised I might have stumbled upon it."

Again Savage paused, this time to attack the nut loaf. Still chewing, he raised his glass and downed most of the Montrachet in one. "After a few months," he continued, "I'd learned some of their language, and I knew the next day was the festival of Manco Capac. I'd managed to bore a small hole in the wall of my hut, and through it I could see the temple door. I had to find out what was in there, to see if my suspicions were correct.

"At sunrise I was woken by low chanting. I peered through the hole, and saw the temple door open. Then, with great ceremony, a shimmering, life-sized gold statue was brought out on a golden carriage. It could only be the lost statue of Manco Capac. I reckoned it must be worth a million pounds, and since then I've discovered it's at least ten times that. But, of course, it was no good to me unless I could escape.

"By now, though, I had a plan. Over the next few weeks I saved some berries and crushed them in a pot to which I added water. As I hoped, the mixture started to ferment. It tasted revolting, but it sure had a kick to it. So one night I invited the guard into my hut, to have a drink. Of course, to allay his suspicions I had to pretend to drink as well, but he had most of it. Finally he finished the booze, belched loudly, and sank to the ground. Within a few minutes he was snoring loudly.

"That was my chance. I climbed over his sleeping body and out of the hut. There was no one around, so I headed into the jungle. I'd have taken the statue with me, but speed was essential. Nearly a year after I was captured, I found my way back to the main trail. There I joined up with a party of Germans who were walking back to Cuzco."

Savage paused to clear his plate. "So that's my story, Mr Raybould. The lost statue of Manco Capac is out there, but only I know where. It's worth at least ten million, and I'll split that with you fifty-fifty. All I need is a hundred thousand to assemble a small expedition. Write me a cheque, and I'll start tomorrow."

Raybould sipped his wine thoughtfully. Savage seemed genuine, and his story appeared plausible. Of course, the thought of stealing the statue from the natives was unpalatable...but did they really have any more right to it than he did? His mind made up, Raybould reached for his jacket pocket.

Savage suddenly started to cough. He put a hand to his throat. His eyes bulged. As Raybould watched, the young man's face began to swell.

"ANDRE!" Raybould shouted. "Ambulance, quick!"

The ambulance arrived within five minutes. The paramedic administered adrenalin, and the swelling immediately started to subside. Savage was rushed to hospital, and it appeared he would survive.

Afterwards, Raybould shook his head. To think he had been about to write the man a cheque there and then. Well, he knew now that Mark Savage was a liar and a con man. He wrote a cheque to the restaurant, including a good tip, and headed for the door.

Raybould decided not to fund the project, having found out in the nick of time that the supposed adventurer was a con man - but how did he know?

SOLUTION

As Savage had been rushed to hospital with a severe allergic reaction to nuts, Raybould knew he had been lying about being taken captive in Peru - for he said he had been forced to live on nothing but nuts and berries for nearly a year.

A Run-In
With Death

A RUN-IN WITH DEATH

Danyon Loader broke through the finishing tape and collapsed in a heap on the track. Reporters and photographers rushed around him and, looking up, Danyon couldn't make out their faces because of the stadium floodlights. He gasped to catch his breath. His coach shoved his way through the crowd and bent over.

"You all right Danyon? Jesus that was a good run! I'm proud of you - you did it!"

He helped Danyon up, put one arm under him and carried him down the tunnel to the dressing rooms. An hour later, Danyon was showered and dressed. His feet were bruised, but otherwise he was fine. He smiled at the coach.

"I did it Pete, I really did it," he said.

A few days later, Danyon was at his London flat, drinking coffee and flicking through some travel brochures. The prize money for winning the 10,000 metres, his first professional win, was sitting in the bank. He could finally afford that holiday he'd always dreamed of - a month's safari in Tanzania.

A week after that, he was all set. At Heathrow, he boarded his plane and, ten hours later, walked out of Dar es Salaam airport into the blinding sunshine. He took a taxi to the Holiday Inn and tried to sleep off his jet lag. He was woken by reception, who told him that his guide was waiting in the lobby. The clock said 10am.

The man waiting for him introduced himself as Ngoko and they shook hands. They had coffee together in the morning room where Ngoko laid out a map and pointed to all the best places to go to see the big five - elephant, lion, leopard, rhino and cheetah. To Danyon, all of it looked wonderful. He nodded and told Ngoko that he was in his hands. Ngoko arranged to pick Danyon up the following morning and said goodbye.

Danyon went to his room and packed his boots, a pair of 'dusters' to wrap around the lower legs, a thermos flask, a wide-brimmed hat and a pair of high-strength binoculars. The following morning, Danyon was ready and waiting outside the Holiday Inn as Ngoko pulled up in a dusty old car. Danyon put his stuff in the back seat next to a large rifle and got in. Ngoko was dressed completely differently, he now wore khaki from head to toe instead of the shirt and trousers he'd worn yesterday. They drove west out of Dar es Salaam and soon hit the open country. Danyon sat back enjoying the hot African sun on his back and the wind in his hair.

On the way, Ngoko explained that there were many more animals in the wild now that international laws prevented poaching. But, he said, there was the new threat of poachers kidnapping or even killing foreigners for their money or their car. That's why he used the same old car, he said patting the steering wheel. "This old baby's been going for years," he said.

The next few days were bliss for Danyon. By day, they drove deeper into the savannah, watching lions, leopards and cheetahs from afar through the binoculars and taking pictures. At night, Ngoko chose a place to stay and they pitched camp, built a fire and prepared the evening meal. In their sleeping bags, Ngoko told Danyon stories about the African wilderness and Danyon listened, amazed.

On the fifth day, they had just struck camp and driven off when the car suddenly stopped. Ngoko tried to start it again, but nothing happened. He looked at the petrol gauge and saw that they had run out of petrol. "No problem," he said, "I have a spare can." He got out, opened the boot and took out a jerrycan. It was empty. Ngoko looked at the can and discovered a hole in the bottom. "Oh my God," he said.

After the initial panic, they looked at the map and calculated that they were 27 kilometres from the nearest town, where there was a petrol pump. They had enough food, but there was only enough water to last one person for a day. They had planned to return to town before the day's end to replenish their water supply. There was a moment of silence as each man thought of the alternatives. Finally, Danyon spoke.

"Look, one of us has to go to the town to get more petrol. I'm an experienced runner, so I should go. It's that simple."

Ngoko looked at him and swallowed. "It's a long way," he said.

"I know. But there's no alternative."

Ngoko nodded.

"I'll take half the water in my flask and the rifle. You stay here, lock the doors and sit tight. Okay?"

"Okay," Ngoko said.

Danyon measured out half the water and picked up the rifle. "See you in a few hours," he said, and ran off.

As he ran, Danyon tried not to think about his predicament, or Ngoko's. He got into a rhythm with his running, not beginning too quickly so that he could cover the distance. He'd run 27 kilometres before, but never in such a dangerous environment and never in such an unforgiving heat. This would be something to tell his grandchildren, he thought.

Two and a half hours later, he saw the town in the distance. Oh thank God, he thought. His whole body was wet with sweat, the insides of his boots, his hair, everywhere. After a few minutes, he hit the outskirts of the town and ran towards the centre. He found the garage and explained to the attendant what had happened. Soon, he was being driven towards Ngoko with two litres of petrol in a new jerrycan.

Half an hour later, they came to the car. Danyon could see Ngoko sitting inside. The windows were rolled up and, when Danyon tried the doors, he found that they were locked. Danyon looked closer and realised Ngoko was dead. There were several bullet holes in his body, but no powder marks, indicating that he had been shot from a distance of at least three of four metres. The car was untouched and there was no sign of forced entry.

If all the windows were up and the doors locked, and there were no bullet holes in the car or signs of forced entry, how had Ngoko been shot?

SOLUTION

He was shot from
outside the car. The
windows may have been
up and the doors locked,
but the roof of the
convertible was down.

90

EXTREME
MEASURES

EXTREME MEASURES

Leonard Adder woke from a deep sleep at exactly 7.25am, rubbed his eyes and walked over to his dresser. He opened the top drawer and pulled out a pair of dark grey socks. From the second drawer, he took out one of twenty identical, white button-down shirts, still wrapped in plastic from the dry cleaners. He opened the door to his closet and ran his fingers over the shoulders of twelve identical, dark grey suits hanging neatly in a row. It wasn't until he was fully dressed and adjusting the knot of his Paisley tie, that he noticed the plane ticket on his bedside table.

"Shoot," he said to himself and started to get undressed.

He'd forgotten that today was the first day of his first holiday in years. His mother had bought him a ticket to Brazil and insisted that he use some of the holiday time that was owed to him by the New York Corporate Financing Firm he worked for downtown. He remembered the conversation word for word.

"You're going to work yourself to death," his mother had said.

"But I like working, Mom," he had answered.

"Don't you read the paper? People are dropping like flies, all across America. They work too hard. Their lives are too stressful."

Leonard had tried to convince her that the idea of white-water rafting down the Xingu river was a more stressful prospect to him than anything he might encounter at the office.

"It's a jungle out there," she had said referring to the world of corporate finance.

"But it's a jungle I'm familiar with. I like my routine," he'd said. "It's comforting to me."

"Nothing like a change to do the body good."

"Mother," he'd insisted. "I..."

"I don't want to hear another word about this, Leonard," she'd cut in. "You're going and that's final."

When Leonard arrived at the airport in Brasilia, he was greeted by an oversized man in a bright orange suit. His name was Brent Starbuck, and he was going to be Leonard's Extreme Vacation team leader.

After two days of hiking and rafting, Leonard had a bad case of trench foot, a partially sprained ankle, a rash that covered his waist and torso, a sore throat, and was running a slight temperature. He spent the last four days of his trip on the porch of the Extreme Vacation lodge under a mosquito net, drinking bottled water and eating high-calorie energy bars.

Leonard had never experienced such a tremendous sense of relief and gratitude as when he finally arrived back at his office building on Madison Avenue. He stood outside and looked up at all of its thirty-two storeys. "What a tall and majestic building," he thought to himself. "And my office is right there," he thought, pointing to a window and admiring the way the city was reflected in the silver-coloured glass.

Leonard arrived at his office and took his seat behind a large oak desk. He picked up the brass nameplate he had been awarded for being Company Employee of the Year, and buffed it with the cuff of his shirt. He leaned back in his leather chair and looked up at the ceiling. He swore to put all manner of adventure behind him. From now on he was going to live a safe and quiet life; he would refuse all holidays; he would work through Christmas and Easter; he would set his alarm even earlier and make sure he was always the first one in the office; he'd be the last one to leave.

As he was thinking these things to himself, Gary, from the office down the hall, knocked on his door and let himself in. "Hey, Tarzan, how was the vacation?"

"Awful," Leonard replied.

"Glad to be back?"

"You don't know the half of it."

While the two men were talking, a thin lick of smoke started to curl around the office floor. Leonard thought he smelt something but chose to ignore it. After a while, Betty, Gary's secretary, came running in. "I think there's a fire," she said.

"It's probably old Perkins on the weed again," Gary said. "He'll never give it up."

"No, I'm serious. Look!" she screamed. "There's smoke billowing into the office from the hall. I'm getting out of here."

"Me too," Gary said. "You coming?" he asked Leonard.

"In a minute," Leonard said. "I don't want to lose these important documents."

"Forget the documents," Gary said, as the fire alarm went off. "Save yourself!" he yelled and ran down the hall.

By the time Leonard had packed his briefcase full of files, the flames had reached his office door, blocking the way to the fire escape.

"Shoot," Leonard thought to himself and closed the door. "How am I going to get out of this one?" And then something strange happened. Leonard remembered something Brent had told him, "You've got to take risks, buddy. Life ain't worth a damn if you don't take risks."

"Why?" Leonard thought to himself. "Why is this happening to me? I am a coward. Why does everyone expect me to be a hero? I don't want to be a hero. I want to be an ordinary guy, but I have no choice."

Leonard looked at the big vista window in his office. He looked at his office door. It was buckling and bubbling with the heat of the flames behind it. The smoke was pouring in, thick and deadly. Leonard looked at the window again and braced himself. He charged towards it, shattering the glass, feeling the heat at his back.

In order to escape the fire, Leonard jumped out the window and, amazingly, he survived. How?

95

SOLUTION

He worked on the ground floor of the 32-storey building and therefore was able to jump out the window and not hurt himself.